HIDDEN CITY HAUNTED CITY

BIRMINGHAM GHOST STORIES

HIDDEN CITY HAUNTED CITY

BIRMINGHAM GHOST STORIES

PETER LEATHER

BREWIN BOOKS

First published by
Brewin Books Ltd, 56 Alcester Road,
Studley, Warwickshire B80 7LG in 2007
www.brewinbooks.com

Reprinted April 2010

ISBN: 978-1-85858-414-0

A Cataloguing in Publication Record
for this title is available from the British Library

Typeset in Baskerville
Printed in Great Britain by
Cromwell Press Group.

CONTENTS

ACKNOWLEDGEMENTS

My thanks go to Ross Crawford, the editor who printed my first Christmas ghost story in *Metronews* in 1995 and is now the Series Editor for all local weeklies, his successors, Bill McCarthy and Damian O'Loughlin (during whose time the title changed to *The Birmingham News*) and the present editor, Victoria Farncombe (much nicer looking than the other three!) who kindly contributed the foreword to this book.

I would also like to thank my former colleague at the University of Birmingham, Dr Elsa Braekkan Payne, director of the Creative Writing programme, who read and commented on several of the stories.

The many people who have contributed to or inspired the stories over the years are, I hope, all mentioned in the introduction – thanks to them all.

I would particularly like to thank my family in Essex who are either very good actors and very kind people or do actually enjoy hearing my latest story each Christmas: Sue and Marten, Mona, Helen and Tom, Simon and Sonia, Edu and Vu.

And finally, thanks of course to everyone at Brewin Books for bringing this project to fruition.

FOREWORD

Everything goes topsy-turvy (or is that turkey?) at newspapers at Christmas time. We hacks like to pretend this is because people are too busy partying and so there's no news to report. This, of course, is complete balderdash.

A far more obvious reason is that the journalists are too busy stuffing themselves with Quality Street and recovering from the office party the night before to care all that much about what's going on in the world.

The deadlines go crazy too. *The Birmingham News* is a weekly paper, which usually goes to press at noon on Wednesdays, but at Christmas, the editorial team are faced with the daunting task of producing three papers in one week so the staff can enjoy the Christmas week off.

So, thank heaven for Peter Leather and his annual ghost story, which has been a popular fixture in the *Birmingham News* Christmas edition since 1995 and saves us work-shy reporters from having to find some more news to write about!

Peter is already a familiar name in the *Birmingham News* as he has been writing a history column for the paper for almost 20 years but, 12 years ago, he asked our editor if he could swap the column for a spooky story, following in the footsteps of Charles Dickens and other writers who liked a good scare at Christmas.

I started at the paper in March 2004 as a lowly trainee reporter so the first yarn I read of Peter's was "Another Sort of Death", a sinister tale set in an old Birmingham pickle factory – Valdemar's. Like all of the stories, the ghosts are fictitious but many of the places and buildings are real – Peter is an architectural expert after all – and half the fun for readers is separating the facts from the fiction.

Valdemar's was a made-up condiment factory in Aston but, ironically, Birmingham's genuine sauce factory – HP – closed down in 2007, another nail in the coffin of the city's manufacturing tradition.

It's the 2005 story, "Invisible Party Line" (great headline, by the way) that is my favourite, though. The mark of a good ghost story is that it sends a chill down your spine and this eerie tale always has me reaching for a comforting toffee penny from the Quality Street tin.

Based on Peter's knowledge of the old telephone exchanges in Birmingham and how callers could sometimes hear each other's conversations on party-lines, it was a popular read that also prompted a mini-campaign in the paper to unearth the truth behind the story.

Now, from my lofty position of News Editor, I'm usually the first person to read Peter's ghost story before sending it to the sub editors to lay out on the page. It will be an honour to read this year's story, the thirteenth one, which will be featuring in this year's Christmas edition of the *Birmingham News* as well as in this book.

Victoria Farncombe, News Editor, *The Birmingham News*

INTRODUCTION

This book brings together twelve ghost stories that have appeared in my *Hidden City* column in the *Birmingham News* and its predecessors each Christmas since 1995. There is also a thirteenth story specially written for the book, which will appear in this year's Christmas edition of the paper.

Hidden City is a column about local history and has been running since 1991, before which I wrote a slightly different sort of column called *Out and About*, which started in April 1988. To mark the 20th anniversary of this next April, a collection of the best bits from the columns will be published by Brewin Books – so I won't say anything more about its history here.

Before I started writing for the paper, I had already written a few ghost and horror stories, so it seemed natural to combine my two interests in this way. I can't exactly remember why I suggested the idea when I did but the then editor, Ross Crawford liked it and that was the start.

I suppose I was trying, in my own little way, to emulate the Christmas ghost stories shown on the BBC in the 1970s, most of which were by the greatest of all writers of ghost stories, M. R. James. I only later discovered that I had been unconsciously copying him by reading the stories to my family each Christmas as he had done to his students!

In keeping with my column's focus on local history and heritage, most of the stories, although totally fictional, have been inspired by some real piece (or place) of Birmingham history. The rest of the introduction will deal with each story in turn, explaining where possible the historical background that lay behind them. I had better just mention that few of the stories originally had titles and these have for the most part been created for the purposes of this book. The reason for this is that newspaper headlines are always added by the sub-editors (subs) in accordance with the amount of space available after the text and any photographs have been page-set. So each story was given a 'headline' rather than a 'title' in the paper and these are recorded below. Two of the headlines were so good that I have adopted them as the titles – "The Angel of Key Hill" and "Dead in Denim" – well done the subs! The three stories that always had titles in my mind were "Last Christmas", "Immortia" and "Invisible Party Line".

One last thing – the sections below contain 'spoilers' i.e. they give away the plots and in some cases the endings – so, if you haven't read the stories yet, you may want to do that first.

1. "Old Habits" (originally headlined "Who walks the corridors now?"), *Metronews*, Thursday 21st December 1995, page 11.

I wasn't sure how Ross was going to react when I suggested writing a Christmas ghost story rather than my usual column. He's a really nice bloke and I've never seen him lose his temper but he's Scottish and I imagined him as a sort of red-faced Alex Ferguson type giving me the hairdryer treatment for daring to suggest such a thing. I even came up with the name 'Cross Rawfood' for him but he wasn't so keen on that and I left it out – he doesn't mind anymore!

Ross is a very keen cyclist and always tries to sneak cycling stories into his papers (readers of the *Solihull News*, where he's working now, will know what I'm talking about!) I'm at the other extreme, never having ridden a bike and once or twice we talked about me learning to ride one as a story for the paper – fortunately for me, it never happened!

The reporter was originally going to be male (i.e. me) and the story was consequently written with 'he', 'him' and 'his' throughout rather than 'she' and 'her' – eagle-eyed readers who track down the original newspaper will see that we left one 'his' in by mistake.

I wasn't sure if there were going to be any more ghost stories after this one so I took the opportunity to name-drop a few friends as people who had written to the paper about spooky goings-on: Mr Bennett is Peter Bennett, the well-known conservationist and historian from Hall Green, Mr and Mrs Snell (John and Anne) are members of my Roman Roads research group

The old Birmingham Accident Hospital, converted to student accommodation in 1995, with the Martin & Chamberlain block of 1871–73 on the left and the original Queens Hospital of 1840–41 on the right.

(see www.brrp.bham.ac.uk) while Mr Cooper is my old friend, Graham Cooper, now an Assistant Headteacher at King Edward's Five Ways. (Funnily enough, the statue of Joseph Sturge, the 19th century Quaker campaigner for peace, electoral reform and the abolition of slavery, did 'move' last year – but only for the purposes of restoration – now he's back).

I chose the old Accident Hospital on Bath Row as the scene of the story because, in 1995, work had just been completed on converting the site into a University of Birmingham hall of residence. The two surviving hospital buildings are the square, classical Queens Hospital of 1840–41 on the right (the oldest remaining purpose-built hospital building in Birmingham) and the Italian Romanesque extension of 1871–73 by famed local architects Martin & Chamberlain on the left. The earlier building bears a coat of arms and the motto 'Cruce quam muro tutior' (I am protected by the cross as by a wall) belonging to the hospital's benefactor, The Reverend Doctor Samuel Wilson Warneford of Bourton-on-the-Hill in Gloucestershire. He was an incredible philanthropist, estimated to have given away over £200,000 (many millions in modern terms) during his lifetime, about £27,000 of which went towards Queens Hospital. Warneford was funding the dream of Birmingham doctor, William Sands Cox (commemorated by a Blue Plaque on the site of his house in Temple Row) who wanted to create a teaching hospital for Queens College medical school, then in Paradise Street.

2. "A Dig in Time" (originally headlined "A grave that told of murder"), *Metronews*, Monday 23rd December 1996, page 10.

Although I have ended up as a Birmingham historian, I actually trained at university to be a Roman archaeologist. That explains why a couple of these stories have archaeological themes and also why local archaeology gets such good coverage in my column – Ross has his bikes and I have my digs! So the principal inspiration for this story was the fact that I knew the long-awaited excavations in advance of the Bull Ring redevelopment would be starting the following year – they commenced in September 1997 and continued until 2001 (you can read all about them in "Beneath the Bull Ring" by Simon Buteux, Brewin Books, 2003).

There wasn't a 'disused factory site' as such but the 'sad little hovels' were based on something else that was in the news that year. This was the growing momentum to get the back-to-backs on the corner of Hurst Street and Inge Street restored, following detailed architectural analysis of the buildings in 1995. In fact, I was not so much thinking of these particular houses but a group on Floodgate Street, which had also been considered for restoration a few years earlier – sadly they were in too bad a state to save and ultimately had to be demolished. The Hurst Street back-to-backs have of course now been magnificently renovated as a National Trust attraction – to find out more go to www.nationaltrust.org.uk and follow the links to them.

I obviously wasn't very up on family history when I wrote this story as it contains a glaring inaccuracy in that respect. As Doreen Hopwood, the city genealogist, has since told me, far from being easy to trace the grave of a poor woman killed in 1826, it would have been virtually impossible. There were no death certificates or census records in those days and, although I might have found her in the burial records of St Martin's, she would undoubtedly have been in an unmarked grave. Of course, the Bull

The Bull Ring digs of 1997–2001 (left) and the Floodgate Street back-to-backs, since demolished (right).

Ring digs were later to exhume hundreds of bodies in St Martin's churchyard but I didn't know that then and, in any case, few of them could be identified. If only I had used a date after Civil Registration was introduced in 1837!

This story also contains a few uses of friends' names: the librarian, Patrick Albutt is a combination of two local history staff at Birmingham Central Library, Patrick Baird and Richard Albutt, while the family involved in the murder are all members of my Roman Roads group – Anne Baker (a.k.a. Anne Snell from the previous story), Kevin Baker (no relation) and Barbara Osborn – they were all quite amused!

3. "Last Christmas" (originally headlined "Victim of haunted house"), *Metronews*, Tuesday 23rd December 1997, page 6.

There was no party as such (at least not one they invited me to!) but it is true that this was the year when the paper moved from Francis Road near Edgbaston Fiveways to the Post and Mail building in Weaman Street. It had

The Francis Road offices of the Daily News/Metronews (left) and the remaining part of the Birmingham Post & Mail building following demolition of the tower (right).

actually happened long before Christmas, in February 1997. *Metronews*, as it was then called (not to be confused with the paper you get on trains and buses these days, which is a different thing) had started out as the *Daily News* in Francis Road in 1984 but became the weekly *Metronews* in 1991. It was taken over by the Post and Mail in 1996, leading to the move the following year.

The premises at 78–79 Francis Road did indeed have a stuccoed Georgian façade but had otherwise been extensively remodelled and extended at the back – they are still there. Ross insists that, having given me permission to use the 'Cross Rawfood' and cycling stuff in explaining the first story, I must now recount the tale of how I managed to back my car at the time, a Citroën 2CV over the edge of the car park behind the basement offices and had to be hauled out by various reporters!

The Post & Mail building was then as now a fairly grim piece of modern architecture (built in 1963–66 by John Madin & Partners) although the jury is out on whether it has been made better or worse by demolition of the tower. It may have been hailed by architectural expert, Andy Foster as "the finest commercial building of its time in the city" (Pevsner Architectural Guides: Birmingham, 2005) but it is seen by others – me included – as one of the principal monuments to an era when Birmingham lost its soul.

The names used in this story are harder to explain. I thought I remembered there being a receptionist in Francis Road called Maria but Ross is pretty sure there wasn't. All I can say is, if your name is Maria and you used to work on reception at the *Metronews* in Francis Road, this one's for you! Whether or not this person existed, McKenzie was definitely not her second name. This may relate to the second influence on the story – my place of work at the University of Birmingham, which was then Winterbourne on Edgbaston Park Road. This fine old Arts & Crafts house of 1903 was the base of the School of Continuing Studies (the adult education department of the University, formerly known as Extra-Mural). I think this is the 'institution' I refer to in the story, although the implication there is that it was a hospital or asylum rather than educational. The ghostly Miss Baird takes her second name from the aforementioned Patrick Baird but was actually based on my then colleague, Dianne Barre, whose rather grand title was Warden of Winterbourne. Her administrative assistant was Irene McKenzie and this may account for the surname of the reporter. That just leaves George, the dead office groper – my friends will be pleased to hear that he is totally made up and not based on anyone I know!

4. "The Angel of Key Hill" (original headline), *MetroNews*, Thursday 24th December 1998, page 14.

This is my favourite story and one of the most personal, dealing as it does with a love betrayed – I'll say no more! Unfortunately, it contains an historical inaccuracy, as Key Hill Cemetery is probably the only one in Birmingham that doesn't have any angels! Pauline Roberts of the Friends of Key Hill Cemetery (go to www.birminghamheritage.org.uk/keyhill.htm to find out more) has kindly been looking into the records to see if there

Key Hill Cemetery – lots of graves and many monuments but no angels!

ever were any angels there – by way of sparing my blushes – but hasn't come up with one as yet. This may be because Key Hill was a nonconformist cemetery and they were not so keen on angels due to their Roman Catholic and High Anglican connotations.

Key Hill is Birmingham's oldest public (i.e. not attached to a church) cemetery having been opened in 1836. Due to the importance of nonconformists in the growth of Birmingham, it contains many of our leading citizens, including Joseph Chamberlain (see story 13). It was closed to burials in 1982 and listed Grade II in 1996. A historical fact-sheet about the cemetery can be downloaded at www.birmingham.gov.uk by following 'Environment', 'Building Conservation' and 'Publications'.

The name Simon Hyde is made up, although I may have had my cousin Simon in mind as he is one of those to whom I read the stories each Christmas.

5. "Nobody Dies at Christmas" (originally headlined "A ghostly Christmas tale" – not one of their best!), *MetroNews*, Thursday 23rd December 1999, page 25.

This is another very personal story and not really to do with Birmingham at all. It's mainly about the death of my mother, almost ten years earlier in

My last family Christmas in Liverpool before Dad died in 1988 and Mum in 1990.

1990, and the task of clearing out the family home in Liverpool, where I had lived since birth. The picture reproduced with the story is the last one I took before leaving the emptied house for the final time – it is looking along the upstairs landing to the door of my parents' bedroom (my father died in 1988). (The photograph of my last family Christmas with Mum and Dad in Liverpool was taken by our friend, Patrick Moloney, who celebrated Christmas with us for many years).

I deliberately didn't use any real names in this, as it was so personal, although my mother's name, Margaret does creep in, albeit for another character. Mum didn't sleep very well and could often be heard clomping up and down the stairs – she wasn't very light on her feet – in the middle of the night. Needless to say, I would sometimes imagine that I could hear her on the stairs when staying in the house after she died – I still do sometimes when I have dreams that I'm back in my bedroom in Liverpool.

The theme about the different generations and not knowing how all the people are related until the end – which I know is probably a bit too complicated for such a short story – was based on musings and discussions I'd had over the years about what people would look like in heaven. After all, my Gran would look like an old lady to me, but surely her husband would see her as the beautiful young woman he married, and her Gran as a little girl. The solution I came up with is that, as spirits, we would look like whatever others expected us to look like – so young, middle-aged and old all at the same time.

If you did find the story hard to understand the first time round, I hope this has cleared things up!

6. "Immortia" (originally headlined "Lost soul caught in the embrace of the earth"), *MetroNews*, Thursday 21st December 2000, page 6.

I first wrote this story, in a much longer form, in the 1980s. I even entered a dramatised version in a BBC competition for new plays – it got through the regional heats but no further. At the time I was torn between academia and writing and had left Oxford, where I had been doing a Doctorate on Roman archaeology, to make a fresh start in Birmingham in 1984. For the first few years I was unemployed, working on various projects, so, when I heard they were looking for volunteers to take part in archaeological excavations at Sandwell Priory in West Bromwich, I signed up. The director was Mike Hodder, now Birmingham's planning archaeologist and a good friend of mine – but he still insists that he can't remember me being there! My experience in the past had been of digs mostly staffed by volunteers, mainly students, but here they were all young unemployed on a Manpower Services Commission scheme – it seemed absolutely typical of Thatcher's Britain.

I hated Margaret Thatcher and blamed her to some extent for the demise of my academic ambitions. Her policies were biting deep both in university archaeology and field units. I had spent a year studying in France in 1982–83 and read a famous article in one of their journals somewhat gloatingly reporting the demise of British archaeology since its glory days in the 1970s, when many French archaeologists had come to Britain to learn from us, and giving the reason in just two words: "Madame Thatcher". (In all fairness, I have to say at this point that Maggie has had the last laugh since the developer-funded approach she espoused has been much more successful than the more idealistic government-funded and hence cash-strapped system used in France).

I also felt the materialistic world of Thatcher's Britain was no place for a writer and thought how such a person would have been better off living

The excavated remains of Sandwell Priory are still visible in the Sandwell Valley, near West Bromwich.

the life of a medieval monk at Sandwell Priory. However, at the same time I appreciated that some of those monks would have been forced into the religious life when they really wanted worldly things and would have loved to live in the 1980s. Hence was born the idea of the working-class poet and the misfit monk who eventually change places to get what they both want.

The title, Immortia is a made up Latin word meant to be the equivalent of 'Undead'. In the longer version of the story, the medieval monks pray, "Oh gracious Lord, God of mercy, grant Thy servant immortality of the spirit and spare him immortia of the body".

A number of burials were unearthed during the excavations at Sandwell Priory but few of them were ordinary monks since their cemetery (spookily numbered Area 13!) was left virtually untouched. The graves in the Chapter House were the high status ones of the Priors while those in the church were members of the local manorial family – women included – who used their wealth and influence to be buried as close to God as they could. There really was one isolated burial found in what appeared to be a drain but this turned out to be a later feature and the burial itself was in a place of honour outside the Chapter House – so much for the misfit monk!

It's also true that the remains were later reburied at All Saints, West Bromwich Parish Church, the Priors in front of the altar and marked by a plaque and the rest in an unmarked grave outside.

(Thanks to Mike Hodder for all the factual background on the digs – if you want to find out more, his report, "Excavations at Sandwell Priory & Hall 1982–88" was published as Volume XXXI of the Transactions of the South Staffordshire Archaeological & Historical Society in 1991).

The slight remains of the Priory have been consolidated and marked with interpretation panels, and there is also a display of finds at nearby Sandwell Park Farm visitor centre.

7. "A Christmas Party Poe-Style" (originally headlined "It's the office a (sic) party to end them all"), *MetroNews*, Thursday 20th December 2001, page 31.

Truth is stranger than fiction they say, and this is a case in point. During 2001 my department at the University, which had moved from Winterbourne to Selly Oak the previous year, was merged with two other departments, the University's School of Education and the remnants of Westhill College, which had been on the Selly Oak site before we got there. Many people in my department and Westhill saw it not so much as a merger as a takeover by the much larger School of Education – something that seemed to be confirmed when it was decided that the new department should be called – surprise, surprise – the School of Education! Needless to say some people resisted the change whereas others were quick to make themselves useful to the new bosses. A team-building exercise was held one day at the Clarendon Suites in Edgbaston – and this is where things got really weird.

When we first arrived, we were offered a flower to wear, its colour depending on which of the three former departments we came from – I refused, which obviously stunned the woman giving out the flowers as she had not been trained to deal with independent thought! Next we were led into an enormous room and told to sit in groups based not on our departments or our subjects but on our star-signs – I kid you not. We were then told to discuss within our groups (I'm a Scorpio by the way) what characteristics we might share in common and how these might help the

The Clarendon Suites in Edgbaston double as a Masonic Temple and are known as the "Home of Warwickshire Freemasonry".

new department. Finally we had to give a performance of some sort which best summarised the outcome of our discussions. Needless to say the 'teachers' were much better at this than the rest of us and our group ended up having to sing "Always Look on the Bright Side of Life". (I only wish I'd been in the group that re-enacted the sinking of the Titanic!)

If all this were not bizarre enough, when I popped out to the toilet, I found a sign on the door urging gentlemen to leave their 'regalia' (or some such word) outside. I did not know then that the Clarendon Suites doubled as a Masonic Temple and were the "Home of Warwickshire Freemasonry".

It's hardly surprising then that, when I came to write that year's ghost story, this unbelievable day was still in my mind and, furthermore, that the thing it most reminded me of was the classic horror tale, "The Masque of the Red Death" by one of my favourite authors, Edgar Allan Poe. The story is therefore a fantastical mixing of the strange but true events that day at the Clarendon Suites with the fiction of the Masque. The colours of the rooms, for example, come straight from the Poe story but also reflect the different colours of flowers they tried to make us wear. The way that people are being turned into mindless zombies is my twist on the inevitable process whereby those who had opposed the merger/takeover gradually had to come onboard for the sake of their careers. I'll leave you to work out for yourselves why the hero's T-shirt has "We Don't Need No Education" on it!

(The picture used with the story is a still from the classic 1925 film "The Phantom of the Opera" in which Lon Chaney, as the Phantom, attends a ball dressed as the Red Death – this was downloaded from Wikipedia under the terms of the GNU Free Documentation License).

8. "The Englishman, the Irishman, the Scotsman and the Welshman" (originally headlined "No Joke Raising The Dead"), *The Birmingham News*, Thursday 19th December 2002, page 31.

Twelve months on and the situation at work had got even worse. The merger had failed and our department was once more separated off under the new title, Centre for Lifelong Learning – hardly very 'lifelong' as it closed down after four years! 'The Devil you know' replaced 'the Devil you don't' of last year's story but in this case the proverb was anything but true. As a result, I was full of anger and bitterness when I wrote this story – the posh word is catharsis. It's a tale of academic infighting and backstabbing à

The University of Birmingham, where I have worked since the 1990s and which has inspired, for good or ill, a number of my stories.

la David Lodge thinly disguised as black magic and murder. The characters and events are highly fictionalised but there really were an Englishman, an Irishman (sort of – one of those tenuous links used by footballers who want to play for the Republic), a Scotsman and a Welshman. I'll leave anyone who thinks they recognise them to decide whether I have been fair or not!

9. "Dead in Denim" (original headline), *The Birmingham News*, Thursday 18th December 2003, page 7.

There's not much to say about this one except that, ghost apart, it is essentially true. In 2001 I moved from my old flat in Edgbaston to a new one in Weoley Castle not far from St Gabriel's church. My bedroom window looks out over the grassy area at the back of the church towards the back fences of the houses on the next road over. I don't know when it first happened but I started seeing this woman hanging around by one of the fences peering through into the garden beyond. She would be there for ten or fifteen minutes, perhaps longer, then I'd look again and she'd be gone. I suppose I should really have gone to the police or social services or, as in the story, informed the people in the house, but instead I made up a

The view from my bedroom window, where I saw the woman who inspired my 2003 Christmas ghost story: the recently installed security fencing should rule out any further sightings – unless she really was a ghost!

ghost story about her. The following year I stopped seeing her. Recently the church has erected security fencing around the grassy area at the rear so there should be no more sightings – unless of course she really was a ghost!

10. "Another Sort of Death" (originally headlined "Pickled Pink At Valdemar's", *The Birmingham News*, Thursday 23rd December 2004, page 7.

Let's got one thing straight right from the start – this story has absolutely nothing to do with Harry Potter! I had never read any of the books or seen any of the films and it was only after the story was published and people started asking me about it that I found out there was a character called Lord Voldemort. My real inspiration was, as with the 2001 story, the works of Edgar Allan Poe, and in particular his tale, 'The Facts in the Case of M. Valdemar', in which a man is hypnotised at the point of death, and his soul thereby trapped within his dead body, still able to communicate with the outside world and pleading to be released.

The Aston Expressway tore the heart out of Aston, creating the landscape of derelict factories featured in the story – I never guessed at the time that HP (top right) might end up being one of them.

(Judging from a quick scan of a few Harry Potter websites, some fans believe that Voldemort was inspired by Valdemar but, apparently, J.K. Rowling says the name was just made up).

The origins of this story were a dream I had in which a friend and I visited an old tractor factory in the countryside which mysteriously came alive around us. I escaped but he stayed behind. (Greg is a made up name as I didn't think my friend would enjoy being cast as someone who was terminally ill!) In order to make the story right for the paper, I transplanted the factory to Birmingham and decided that Aston was the ideal location. I haven't been here long enough to remember old Aston but I have heard lots of tales and seen lots of photographs of how it had the heart torn out of it by the building of the Expressway. I've also driven around the area enough times to see the isolated old buildings, such as the Bartons Arms, cut off from their original neighbours, the derelict or demolished factories and the odd little rows of houses, shops and pubs somehow still surviving from the many thousands that were once there. (In fact, I did just that looking for a photograph to accompany the story in this book).

The one thing I could not have foreseen back in 2004 was that HP might one day become a real ghost pickle factory.

11. "Invisible Party Line" (originally headlined "Ghostly tale of wrong number"), *The Birmingham News*, Thursday 22nd December 2005, page 6.

This is another story which, like Immortia, had been written years before I used it in the paper. The original longer version dated back to 1987 and was, I must confess, a much raunchier affair aimed at the men's magazine market, although never published.

My initial inspiration was an old phone we had back home in Liverpool with a little silver button on top, which my parents explained dated back to the days when we were on a party line with one of our neighbours and needed to press the button to clear the line. (Not that I'm bragging but we were the first people in our street to have a phone!) The other thing that stuck in my mind was that our local telephone exchange, whose first three letters featured in our phone number until all-digit numbers were introduced, had a name that had once been that of the district but had

The Priory telephone exchange at Northfield (left) and what's left of the large Victorian house after which it may have been named (right).

fallen out of use, so that, unless you knew, you could not easily work out which part of the city someone with our number lived in.

When I had to transpose the story to Birmingham, I started researching old telephone numbers to see if there were any similar cases here, where the exchange name did not automatically give away the area of the city it was in. As luck would have it, I didn't have to look very far as the answer turned out to be my very own exchange, now 475 but formerly PRI for Priory. Following publication of the story, I did further research and devoted a couple of columns to unravelling the real mystery of why Northfield telephone exchange was called Priory and not simply Northfield.

The answer came partly from Mike Fletcher, who runs the www.telephonesuk.co.uk website on which I had first found out about the

Priory exchange, and partly from local historian and former BT man, Ted Rudge, whom I have known for years and who features in the story as the neighbour, Ted. The first part of the question was easy to answer: when the NORthfield exchange was opened in 1933 there was already a NORthern exchange in Handsworth and, since they had the same first three letters, a different name was needed for the sake of the dialling code. But why Priory? I never found a definitive answer to this but Ted showed me an old map on which the land adjacent to the exchange was owned by a large house on the Bristol Road known as The Priory, only the Gothic doorway and garden steps of which now survive. It was never a real priory (although ironically owned for many years by a Roman Catholic convent) but rather one of many cases in Birmingham and elsewhere where the name was given to a large house as an affectation (the same is also true of many houses called Abbey, Grange etc). No reason has emerged as to why this particular house should have given its name to the telephone exchange but it seems the likeliest explanation.

Going back to the story, the names of the murderous husband and his doomed wife are derived from my cousins Sue and Marten Bayly who are among the family members mentioned in the acknowledgements who get to hear my ghost story read out each Christmas – there was a lot of laughter in the room when their names came up in this one!

12. "Never at Night" (originally headlined "The cemetery gates appeared locked…"), *The Birmingham News*, Thursday 21st December 2006, page 16.

I really do walk past Lodge Hill cemetery almost every working day, on the way to work in the morning and on the way home at night. Since the story was published I have started walking though the cemetery on nice days, although I had not done this before. The other strange, psychological effect of the story is that I do tend to walk on the other side of the road from the railings on dark nights! One night I didn't do this and, as I was passing close by the railings, something suddenly loomed up out of the darkness on the other side: as you can imagine, I got quite a fright; but it was only a helium balloon that someone had attached to one of the graves.

Lodge Hill Cemetery needs the sort of Friends that Key Hill and Brandwood End have to save its crumbling Victorian mortuary chapels.

One of my students, Janet Sullivan was so determined to check the accuracy of the historical background to this story that she went to see for herself if there really were fleur-de-lis rather than crosses on the railings – there are! What there isn't, is a side gate leading into the service yard.

Lodge Hill Cemetery was opened in 1895 when Kings Norton & Northfield was an Urban District Council separate from Birmingham – this changed with the expansion of Birmingham in 1911. A crematorium was opened on the site in the 1930s and there are still cremation burials there even though there is no room for any new inhumations. The original chapels are in a bad state and, unfortunately, do not as yet seem to have attracted the sort of local support shown by the Friends of Brandwood End Cemetery for the restoration of their chapels (see next story).

13. "Number 13" (to be included in the Christmas 2007 edition of *The Birmingham News*).

All of the previous stories were written in December shortly before publication, although in some cases I had been mulling over them for a while, but this one had to be written in June to meet the needs of the book publisher. It's not so easy to think dark thoughts in June as in December! There was also a need, not present in the other stories, to create something that would bind them all together. But perhaps the biggest difference is that, in this case, I am writing the explanation of the story before writing the story itself – I thought I should leave that for last.

The first thing to occur to me was the title, obviously because it's the thirteenth story but also as a tribute to M. R. James, whom I have already mentioned as my inspiration for writing Christmas ghost stories, since one of his stories is called "Number 13". (The subject matter of this is entirely different from mine, dealing as it does with a hotel in Denmark where a room of this number, not there during the day, mysteriously appears at night).

My original thought was that 13 would be a house number but I was struggling to come up with anything to do with a haunted house that hadn't already been done a million times before. Then one day I was walking past Lodge Hill cemetery as I do (see above!) when I saw a bus parked at a bus stop outside – it all clicked into place: a Number 13 bus that circulates between Birmingham's cemeteries at night allowing the dead to pay visits to each other!

After discussion with Alan Brewin, the publisher, we decided that a picture of an old Birmingham bus outside or better still inside an old cemetery would be ideal for the book cover. I first contacted the people at Aston Manor Road Transport Museum but, while they were keen to help, the only Birmingham bus they had available was undergoing extensive repairs. They suggested various other options but, as if by magic, the solution found me – literally. I was crossing the Hagley Road that Sunday when, out of the blue, an old Birmingham bus drove past. Needless to say I ran after it up Monument Road to Waterworks Road where it stopped (it was taking people from Sarehole Mill to Perrott's Folly as part of a Tolkien Weekend). Talk about running for the bus!

When I got my breath back I explained my interest to the 'conductor', Chas Pugh and he put me in touch with his bosses at Travel West Midlands, who were happy to participate.

I then needed to obtain permission from the cemetery. My first thought was to do it at Lodge Hill since that was my 'local' and where I had the idea in the first place. However, the bus was based at Yardley Wood and that made Brandwood End Cemetery the best option. Although I've written about Brandwood End in my column more than once, I had never actually visited. Having obtained permission from the cemetery authorities, I went to have a look and it was perfect – so good in fact that photos from Brandwood have ended up in several of the stories, including 'The Angel of Key Hill!'

The one problem was the weather – not the usual one of it not being good enough but it being too good. We wanted all the photos in the book, and especially the front cover, to be a bit sombre and gloomy – so blue skies and sunshine were out. Fortunately for us, if not everyone else, the storms towards the end of June were ideal and the photo-shoot took place on Monday 25th – sort of fitting as six months either way from Christmas Day (you may have seen the pictures of us on the front-page of that week's *Birmingham News*). Thanks to Travel West Midlands, Chas Pugh and driver, Derrick Hughes for their help in this, Andrea Haines and Dawn Harding for permission to use Brandwood End and Anne Courbet of the Friends for putting me in touch with them.

For bus enthusiasts, the vehicle is a 55-seater Daimler CVG6, registration number MOF 225, which came into service in June 1954 and worked until the late 70s, ending up on the Outer Circle. It is now used for historical activities, filming and hire – for more details ring Chas Pugh on 0121 254 6405.

When I first came up with the idea for the story, I assumed that there would never have been a real Number 13 bus, for reasons of superstition, but it turns out there was. According to Malcolm Keeley's book on Birmingham City Transport (Transport Publishing Company, 1977), the 13 came into service in 1923 running between Sparkbrook and Yardley Wood Road. In 1925 the route was extended to start in the city centre and, in 1929, a 13A was introduced running between the city centre and Yardley Wood (ironically where the vintage bus is now based).

Old bus, old cemetery: Travel West Midlands' vintage 1954 double-decker parked up in Brandwood End Cemetery for the cover photo for this book.

Brandwood End Cemetery was opened in 1899 and, like Lodge Hill, was in Kings Norton & Northfield Urban District until absorbed by Birmingham in 1911. It was listed as a historic site in 1997. One of the key aims of the Friends of Brandwood End Cemetery, formed in 2005, is the restoration of the mortuary chapels – you can find out more on their website at www.fbec.org.uk.

There are eleven cemeteries within the City of Birmingham (including Sutton Coldfield) and I had some fun working out a bus route to join them all up. It was my intention to have the ghosts of various famous Brummies getting on the bus at the different cemeteries but, after discussing this with Patrick Baird, I realised that, with the obvious exception of Key Hill, where the principal occupants are well known, it would have taken a lot of research to track down such people in all the others. (There is clearly a book to be written here – where to find the graves of famous Brummies – but it's not my sort of thing so I hope someone else will have a go!) I decided to settle on a brief cameo by the instantly recognisable Joseph Chamberlain (although, as Ross Crawford said when I ran this past him, "Joe Chamberlain wouldn't be seen dead on a bus!") and otherwise people the bus with ordinary Brummies and characters from the other stories. The cemeteries are listed, and some historical background given, at www.birmingham.gov.uk/cemeteries.bcc. As with Key Hill, there are historical fact-sheets on Brandwood End, Handsworth and Warstone Lane downloadable at www.birmingham.gov.uk, 'Environment', 'Building Conservation', 'Publications'.

The Bear & Staff pub on the Bristol Road in Selly Oak is our regular watering hole and has witnessed some memorable drinking sessions – especially on the day the University closed down our department.

Finally, it's very fitting that my character should get off the bus, at the end, at Kings Norton Cemetery in Longdales Road, which is Birmingham's newest cemetery, opened in 2005. As regular readers of *Hidden City* will know, excavations during development of the site revealed important Roman remains (for more information go to www.birmingham.gov.uk/archaeology.bcc and follow the links to 'Birmingham's Archaeology', 'Roman Birmingham' and 'Kings Norton') – so what better place for a Roman archaeologist to spend eternity?

OLD HABITS

"Ghosts!" shouted the editor, "You want me to put ghosts on the front page of my newspaper? Get on your bike!"

The chastened reporter did just that. It might be December but she was sticking to her pledge not to drive a car all year. She fumed silently to herself as she unchained her beloved bicycle.

The story about ghosts was a good one – she'd put a lot of effort into researching and writing it. For whatever reason there really did seem to be a huge upsurge in the number of reported ghost-sightings in Birmingham this year.

It had started with letters to the paper – dozens of them – from ordinary, sane Brummies who had witnessed something uncanny. There was Mr Bennett of Hall Green who reported strange misty shapes floating along the River Cole, Mr and Mrs Snell of Moseley who had seen a whole legion of spectral Roman soldiers marching along an unseen road in their back garden, and many, many more.

But the editor of City News was adamant: "Get me some hard facts", he said, "And then I'll print your story".

Out onto the icy roads the reporter cycled, her mind filled with all the interviews, the midnight watches and graveyard shifts – but still nothing.

Round Fiveways she went, dodging through the heavy traffic which seemed, as always, intent on knocking her down. She glanced over at the statue of Joseph Sturge – a Mr Cooper had written to the paper claiming to have seen it moving.

She cycled along Islington Middleway and left up Bath Row. She was gazing a little too intently at the old Accident Hospital, now student

residences, wondering why a building with such a history had not yet featured in the mailbag, when a car hit her.

The next few hours were a mixture of semi-conscious experiences and dreamlike images drawn from her current obsession. In the real world she glimpsed doctors and nurses busying themselves around her in some unrecognisable casualty ward; in her dreams they wore the smock coats and long dresses of a bygone age.

At long last she awoke in a clean, crisp bed, in a typical modern city hospital. When she was ready they told her what had happened. She had nearly died out there in Bath Row, and they weren't quite sure why she hadn't. The ambulance had been held up in the traffic and by the time they got there she should really have bled to death. But someone had carried her into the old Accident Hospital and expertly bound her wounds – the funny thing was that none of the students who now lived there had any idea who it could have been.

The reporter smiled – perhaps she had her front-page story after all.

A DIG IN TIME

People have this image of archaeologists digging among classical ruins in the Mediterranean. Bearded men surrounded by scantily clad young female students. Sun, sand and sections.

It's not like that in reality. More like a wet December day in Digbeth with a bunch of people so covered up you can't tell if they're men or women. More Corporal Jones than Indiana Jones.

But occasionally something happens that makes it all worthwhile – an important find, your picture in the paper – or maybe, just once in a lifetime, something so special that you'll never forget it.

For me it happened right here in Birmingham, digging on a disused factory site not far from the Bull Ring. There had been houses there once, sad little hovels where the town's poorest workers lived. The Industrial Revolution had its price.

We were excavating a cellar when we found it – a human skeleton, white, worn and very, very small. It was a child – a little girl – buried beneath the floor of the house over 150 years ago.

You get used to finding "stiffs", as we call them, but this one was different – so small, so weak, so vulnerable.

There was something else different too – this one spoke to me.

Don't get me wrong, I'm not talking about some ghostly voice issuing out of the skull. It was more subtle than that – so subtle in fact that perhaps you'll say I imagined it all.

I was preparing the site report on my word processor that night when I suddenly realised that instead of "female skeleton 95cm in length" I had in fact typed "Help Me Find My Mother".

That gave me the shivers. I decided I'd been working too hard and went to bed. Bad idea – at 3am I woke screaming and sweating from a nightmare in which a drunken man was beating his wife and then clubbed his own daughter to death when she tried to stop him.

The next day was Saturday, and I spent it in the Central Library looking at old newspapers. One of the staff, Patrick Albutt, had an interest in local murders and pointed me in the right direction.

It didn't take long to find the story I was looking for, in a paper dated December 23, 1826: "Grisly Find in River Rea. Woman's Body Dragged From Water".

Subsequent editions told the story of how 29-year-old Annie Baker had been murdered by her husband, Kevin, in a drunken rage. There was a daughter too, Barbara, but of her no trace had been found.

Until now.

It was easier than I'd thought it would be to track down Annie's grave. After that it was just a matter of convincing the coroner that the skeleton we'd dug up really was her daughter, Barbara, and then getting permission to reopen the grave and let the two lie together at long last.

Then it was time to get back to archaeology. I finished the site report with a heavy heart and typed in those ultimate words, "The End" – except, when I checked it again the next morning, two different words were at the bottom of the page: "Thank You".

LAST CHRISTMAS

It really was going to be the party to end all parties this year. Next day the newspaper was moving lock, stock and barrel to new premises.

Maria McKenzie had only been on the staff as a junior reporter for six months but she had grown really fond of the old building with its peeling Georgian facade.

And now they were moving to a big soulless office block with no history beyond the 1960s.

Maria loved old buildings and had already written several stories for the paper highlighting conservation issues – once or twice they'd even done some good!

But the story she really wanted to write, the one she'd been waiting all her life to write, you could say – well, the editor wouldn't have it.

The problem wasn't that the subject of her story was yet another old, crumbling building but that this one was haunted – and the editor didn't believe in ghosts.

She'd known about the house – in Edgbaston near the University – since she was a scared child being dared by her friends to venture in after dark.

It was a big house, built for one of the city's luminaries at the turn of the century, but used as an institution for many years. It was said that the earthbound spirit of a former warden, a Miss Baird, was to be seen at night, endlessly walking the corridors and climbing up and down the stairs as she had in life.

She'd researched the history, tracked down eyewitnesses and even arranged to spend the night there – but the editor still wasn't interested. Ah well, maybe next year.

78

Anyway, now it was party time, and a chance to say goodbye to the old office and wish her colleagues and friends a happy Christmas – there was lots to eat and plenty to drink, so ghosts could take a back seat.

But still, as the night drew on, her mind kept on going back to the old house and its desperate revenant, doomed to remain on the earthly plain until some task unfulfilled in life could finally be completed.

Her musings were rudely interrupted by a groping hand on her bottom and a slurred voice in her ear: "Come on Maria, give us a kiss for Christmas – I can't go until you let me".

It was George, the Sales Manager, who'd been pursuing her since she first arrived at the paper. Now he was drunk and looking even more unkempt than usual. But there was something in his eyes so sad that she inexplicably felt sorry for him. Closing her eyes and holding her breath she gave him what he wanted – and then he was gone.

She was drifting back into her melancholy thoughts about lost souls again when suddenly the room went silent. The editor was making an announcement – before he'd finished Maria had fainted. He'd been telling them how poor old George had been killed in a road accident on the way to the party.

THE ANGEL OF KEY HILL

He fell in love with an angel in Key Hill Cemetery.

But Simon Hyde was no romantic – he was a thief, specialising in antique statuary. And the angel was an expensive marble monument hidden away in the darkest corner of the cemetery, far from prying eyes and ideal for a quiet visit in the dead of night.

So Simon and a few friends (fifty quid a time) set out with the tools of their trade at 3am one moonless December morn to relieve the angel of its endless vigil.

It was easier than they expected – those Victorians knew a thing or two about anchoring their monuments down but this one was a doddle. What made all the difference was the unusual siting of the angel, not at the head of the grave but astride it, where the soil had long ago been disturbed.

"Someone down there's helping us", one of them joked – but not Simon. He was staring through the blackness at the headstone, worn to crumbling, trying to decipher the one word inscription – was it "Unforgotten?"

The job done, they loaded the 'liberated' angel on their wagon and took it back to Simon's ground floor flat, where he stood it by his bed.

The dreams started that very night – a beautiful woman, who seemed to love Simon as much as he instantly loved her.

"Do you know who I am?" she asked, but Simon didn't know or care.

Each night for a week she returned, asking the same question, and each day he sat alone, staring endlessly at the marble angel.

Finally he made the connection and it broke his heart – she was the woman in the grave: the one woman he had ever really loved and he could never have her.

GEORGE BEECH J.P.

"There may be a way", she told him that night, "Death is no real barrier to true love. It can be done, if you really want it".

Simon wanted it more than anything he had ever wanted in his life. "Tomorrow is my birthday", she said, "Come for me then".

At three o'clock in the morning, when they had first "met", Simon returned to Key Hill Cemetery. But there were no crowbars or jemmies this time, just the power of his love.

He waited by her grave, gazing down at the gouge where the angel had stood. He didn't know what to expect – a cracking of the earth as she rose majestic or something more spiritual.

"Do you love me", asked her voice in his head, "do you love me more than life itself?" "Yes", cried Simon, again and again.

Something began to happen. He felt a physical presence very close behind him but didn't dare look round.

When he heard his beloved's voice again it was no longer in his head but real and very near, a little dry and cracked perhaps but beautiful nonetheless.

"My poor, poor darling", it said – as she spoke he found his eyes drawn to the worn headstone whose inscription no longer seemed to be "Unforgotten" but "Unforgiven" – "do you not see?" – he began to turn, love rapidly becoming terror – "the angel was not there to protect me, it was there to keep me in".

NOBODY DIES AT CHRISTMAS

"Nobody dies at Christmas!" The voice was strained and the eyes not far from tears, so it seemed best not to say anything else. It was going to take Lizzie some time to come to terms with her little sister not being there.

George and Margaret had thought long and hard about cancelling everything but, with so many members of the family here, they just had to go on, even without Jennie.

Down in the living room the various Uncles and Aunts, Nephews and Nieces, Cousins and In-Laws sat uneasily together as an air of sadness permeated the house.

Margaret sat alone upstairs looking at a picture of a grey-haired old woman. How she wished she had taken the trouble to visit her more often. It was times like these that made you realise how much families matter.

George busied himself around the place, polishing stuff which didn't need polishing, dusting stuff which had never seen dust – it was his way of keeping his mind off things. He felt his share of guilt too. He should never have left Jennie alone like he did.

Lizzie was taking it worst of all. She'd been looking forward so much to seeing Jennie again. She'd never wanted them to be separated in the first place and had been counting the days until they were back together.

In a room on the other side another member of the family was alone with her thoughts. She desperately wanted to be with them but here she was in her sickbed, barely able to move. She prayed they would come for her.

It was time for them all to gather, all the generations together. George and Margaret had managed to compose themselves in their different ways

but Lizzie was inconsolable. Everyone wanted to say the right thing but no one knew what it was.

Suddenly there was a loud thump over their heads. There was only one person it could be. No one moved.

The noises were on the stairs now – slow, painful steps. George looked at the door with a mixture of fear and anticipation. Margaret thought of the kindly old face in the photo and began to weep.

Finally the door opened. They all saw something different there: Lizzie her beloved sister as she had been when they were children; George his wartime widow, beautiful in her bridal gown; Margaret the mother who had raised her single-handed only to be left alone in her old age.

Lizzie rose to her feet and rushed over as the figure finally emerged from the dark tunnel of the hallway and stepped into the light. "Oh Jennie, you made it", she cried, the tears running down her cheeks, "Come and meet your family – just the ones you know in here, but there are thousands more outside".

Jennie looked bemused by it all, as well she might – she too thought nobody ever died at Christmas.

IMMORTIA

"The dead rest easy. They lie on the earth and the earth lies on them. But there are some, the restless dead, who find no peace in the grave".

She wept as she read the tattered scrap of paper. She stood beside an unmarked grave thinking of the man who wrote those words.

It was twenty years ago and they were teenagers – left school at sixteen and straight on Maggie's scrap heap – but, though their pockets were empty, their hearts were full.

He didn't care about money. He was a poet. His father despaired.

Strange then that it was the hated Job Centre that changed their lives.

Instead of the usual shelf packing and road-sweeping, they told him about a scheme to get unemployed people involved in an archaeological dig on the site of a medieval priory.

It appealed to the Gothic romantic in him and he signed up straightaway. The fact that the first day was drizzly, cold and muddy only seemed to make it better.

The one part he didn't like was digging up the graves of the monks – he reckoned they deserved better.

Instead he was assigned to excavate a drain outside the priory – which is where, of course, he found the body.

But he didn't mind working on this one. He nicknamed him the "misfit monk" and identified with him completely – after all, he'd been thrown on the scrap heap too.

He worked on the skeleton by day, and in the evenings he wrote a poem about a man forced to enter a monastery by his father though he longed for worldly things.

She saw him less and less those days – and one night she didn't see him at all.

They found him next morning crouched over the grave, staring into the skull's empty eye-sockets.

He seemed to be in a trance but leapt up the minute she touched him. He pushed her aside, told the archaeologists where they could stick their job and stormed off.

That night he told her he was going to marry her, and six months later he did.

In the meantime he 'got on his bike' and got a job in a small business, which, within five years, he was running. He bought her everything money could buy.

He tore up and burned his last poem with the exception of the one scrap she managed to save.

The year after they were married she attended the ceremony to rebury the skeletons from the priory – she didn't dare tell him she was going.

And she continued to go secretly each year to the unmarked grave to lament her lost teenage love.

She read the scrap again: "The dead rest easy. They lie on the earth and the earth lies on them. But there are some, the restless dead, who find no peace in the grave".

And one of those poor creatures, she thought, lies buried here – the body of a misfit monk and the soul of a working class poet.

A CHRISTMAS PARTY POE-STYLE

This is going to be the office Christmas party to end them all, he thought, as he stepped into the darkness.

The strange scene instantly reminded him of something – but he couldn't think what.

He recognised so few people – the takeover had seen to that – and even those he'd known for years were somehow not the same anymore.

The fancy dress didn't help either! It was typical of the new management that even the Christmas party had to be used as a 'team-building' exercise.

"Come as you see your role in the team", had been the instructions, "It will help us learn about each other".

He was wearing his tattiest jeans and a Pink Floyd T-shirt reading "We Don't Need No Education".

He had to admit, though, that the transformation of the offices was quite astonishing. It must have taken all night to prepare – but there had been no shortage of volunteers wanting to make a good impression on the new boss. A lot of people seemed to be putting in for night work these days – he hardly saw anyone he knew during the day anymore.

The party was being held in seven rooms each decked out in a different colour, with lighting to match. The idea was that you chose the room with the colour most suiting your mood. He was told, in hushed tones, that there was a totally black one at the end, and made straight for it.

First there was blue, then purple, then green, then orange, then white, then violet. The black room – in fact the boss' office – was more a deep scarlet red, once your eyes adjusted to the candlelight.

He was alone in there – hardly surprising given the sombre surroundings – and wondered why he'd not yet been summoned during office hours like so many of his colleagues. Remembering their drained faces and blank expressions when they emerged, he was perhaps lucky he hadn't.

He heard a noise behind him and turned to find himself facing a gaunt figure in a blood-red cowl and skull face-mask. He was sure it must be the boss and, determined to show he wasn't scared of him like the rest, stepped forward and pulled off the mask.

The last free thought he ever had was a quote: "And Darkness and Decay and the Red Death held illimitable dominion over all".

THE ENGLISHMAN, THE IRISHMAN, THE SCOTSMAN AND THE WELSHMAN

There was an Englishman, an Irishman, a Scotsman and a Welshman. I know it sounds like a bad old joke – but this story is anything but funny.

I was the Englishman and all four of us worked for the same firm. The Irishman was a real gent, old school, good manners and someone who really cared about the customers. The Scotsman – I'll come back to him. The Welshman was the boss, a real smarmy type with thousand pound suits and hundred pound hairdos.

The Scotsman was second-in-command. He'd been second-in-command to the old boss and was none too happy to have been overlooked for the top job. And when he was unhappy he couldn't take it out on the Welshman – at least not to his face – and it was water off a duck's back to the Irishman – so he'd have a go at me.

The thing was, he was half my size, so there'd only have been one winner if it ever came to blows. But we both knew he was the type of man who wouldn't fight back but would simply have me sacked and probably sued as well.

You see, I was his junior – which meant I did all the work and he took all the credit.

It also meant – and this was his biggest mistake – that when he started plotting against the Welshman, he expected me to help.

When I say help, I mean I did all the risky stuff and signed my name to things so, if we got caught, I'd be the fall guy.

But it was an educational experience all the same. Give the Scotsman his due, he wasn't planning to push the Welshman under a bus or tamper with the brakes on his car – nothing as simple as that. Instead he'd decided to put a curse on him!

I was the one who had to go to the occult shops, read all the musty old Latin books and do despicable things in graveyards at night. The only thing is, I was learning more about black magic than the Scotsman ever knew.

The curse worked like a treat and the Welshman was dead within a month – I won't say how, but it wasn't very pleasant.

The Scotsman finally got what he'd always wanted – the boss's job. He actually turned up at midnight on the day of his appointment to try out the chair for size – I knew he would and I was there too, hiding in the shadows.

I didn't care to look at what happened when he sat down. I just listened to the screams.

That's the funny thing about magic – you can kill people with it but you can also use it to raise the dead.

DEAD IN DENIM

She was there again, regular as clockwork, in the misty light of dawn. A slight, slim figure with blonde hair. Hard to put an age to her – maybe twenties or thirties – especially since she was wearing that ageless outfit of denim jacket and jeans.

She was where she always was, her face pressed to a crack in the back garden fence of the house opposite.

As usual, there didn't seem to be anyone there for her to be looking at. I had a much better view from my elevated position in my first floor back bedroom.

I never stared at her for any length of time, just the occasional glance, until one time I'd look and she'd be gone – until the next morning.

It had been going on for weeks now. I'd thought several times of calling the Police – but she didn't seem to be doing any harm.

I'd begun to make up my own story about why she was there – a mother whose children had been adopted or taken away from her for some reason. She'd tracked them down to this house and was hoping to catch a glimpse of them.

I didn't want to be an interfering nosey neighbour, but I'd finally decided to go and knock on the door. I had to tell them, didn't I? In case she was dangerous or something.

I made my way round and knocked. I didn't know what to say when the door was opened by a pretty young woman – so I just blurted out what I'd seen and what I suspected.

The woman was livid – she asked me what business of mine it was judging her family. She'd have me know that her kids were her own and they had a

father too! In order to cover my embarrassment, I tried describing the woman – and that made her even angrier, but in a different way.

She asked me if I was playing some sick joke and had her dad put me up to it? She said he'd never forgiven her for turning her mother away when she'd come looking for help, even if she was a drug addict and had been knocking her about all her life. I should go and tell the old b that it was only after years of treatment and doctors that she had stopped blaming herself for her mum's suicide. Then she slammed the door in my face.

I wandered home in a daze, trying to make sense of it all. I couldn't sleep that night, pondering impossible questions.

At the crack of dawn I ran to the window and stared out. The woman in denim was there as usual. But this time she turned and stared right up at me. As her figure floated up towards my window, the ghastly look on her pallid face told me she knew what I had done and was as angry as the place where she undoubtedly came from.

ANOTHER SORT OF DEATH

"I'm fifty tomorrow and I want to go to Valdemar's".

It had been forty years since I'd heard the voice at the other end of the phone but it was unmistakably my childhood best mate, Greg, who I grew up with in Aston.

"Have you been back recently", I asked, "There's a tower block where our street used to be!"

"I know", he said, "But surely Valdemar's is still there?"

We were strangers when he picked me up the next day, but soon we were joking and laughing like it was yesterday.

All the same, it was weird heading up the Expressway together and even weirder turning off into the concrete maze they'd made of our home.

Only then did we start talking about Valdemar's.

Every year we'd gone there on a school outing. It was only the local pickle factory – albeit with the grand name of "Valdemar Preserves" – but to us kids it was like a magical and mysterious fairy-tale castle. Our nans told us they could preserve anything there, and we were both fascinated and frightened by what that might mean.

Best of all Old Mr Valdemar would let us go on all the machines and sample his latest products.

That's what Greg wanted to relive on his fiftieth birthday.

I told him it must have been knocked down years ago and, even if it hadn't, Mr Valdemar would be long dead. But he just kept on driving round until he found what he was looking for – sort of.

In a tiny bit of old street amid the tower blocks was the factory – a derelict ruin.

Greg still insisted we had to go in. There was a hint of desperation in his voice that worried me.

It was as deserted as it looked. Greg began to cry. "I just had to see if it was true they could preserve anything", he sobbed, "The doctor only gave me a few months".

I put my arm around his shoulders. Just then I noticed that one corner of the room was a bit less derelict that it had first seemed. There were clean tiles on a wall that I thought had only been bare brick. Out of the shadows stepped a figure – it was Old Mr Valdemar, looking exactly like he did when we were kids.

"Good day to you young man", he said to Greg, ignoring me, "Have you come to sample my preserves?"

He stretched out his hand and Greg took it. Out of the corner of his eye and mouth he looked at and spoke to me. This close up I could see the unnatural yellowish tint of his skin. "Thank you for bringing him", he said, "But I think you had better go now. Perhaps I will see you again one day?"

I was out the door like a ten-year-old and half-a-mile away before I looked back. Of Valdemar's factory there was no sign. Just tower blocks and an unkinder sort of death.

INVISIBLE PARTY LINE

"My husband's been acting very strangely – I'm scared he might hurt me".

I looked at my phone in utter incomprehension. I'd just picked up the receiver to call a friend and this woman's voice was on the line ...

"Is there anyone there?"

I was silent for about thirty seconds weighing up whether I should just put the phone down but then I spoke.

"I'm sorry, I think you've got a wrong number – who were you trying to call?"

"Oh Thank God", she said, "I thought he'd done something to the phone. Are you the Police?"

"No", I said, "Just a private number. I think you need to redial".

"Please don't go", she pleaded, "It's taken ages to get through to anyone – can you call the Police for me?"

"OK", I said, hesitantly, "Who are you?"

"My name is Susan Bailey and my number is Priory 28..."

The line went dead.

I couldn't sleep that night worrying what to do. I had a name but no address – unless of course "Priory" was a house or street name – but why did she say it was her number?

I was going to feel a right nana telling the Police this – it was probably a hoax – but what if she really was in trouble?

I decided it might be easier to explain things in person so set out next morning for the local Police station.

In the street I bumped into my neighbour, Ted. It struck me he was a retired phone engineer and might be able to help.

TELEPHONE EXCHANGE.

I didn't want him to think I was crazy so I just said there'd been a voice on the line when I picked up the phone.

"That takes me back", he chuckled, "It sounds like when people had party-lines".

"Party-lines?"

"Yeah, in the old days, when there weren't enough lines to go round, you might have to share with a neighbour – a party-line, they called it – so sometimes when you picked up your phone, they'd be on. Come to think of it, I do believe your house and the one opposite were the first round here to have phones, so you were probably on a party-line with them – but that would have been years ago, back in the old Priory days".

"Priory?" I asked, almost gasping.

"Yeah", said Ted, "The first three digits you dial today are the local exchange but before 1966 we used letters – round here it was PRI for Priory. Are you OK? You look like you've seen a ghost!"

"I'm fine", I lied, "But one other thing – did anything weird ever happen in the house across the road?"

He laughed – "You mean you've never heard of the 'Christmas Murder' back in 1955 when Martin Bailey strangled his wife! People still talk about it. Are you really OK? You're white as a sheet".

I didn't answer, just stared over at the house opposite. There was no use going to the Police now – I was already fifty years too late.

NEVER AT NIGHT

Every day he walked home past Lodge Hill Cemetery.

In the summer it was great – sometimes he would even detour through the cemetery to enjoy the grass and trees – but in the winter it was dark and a bit spooky and he stayed outside on the road.

Then one night he heard someone calling him.

It was a shock at first when he saw the white faces looking out from inside the cemetery but then he realised it was just a couple of kids, a boy and girl, about 11 or 12, pressed against the railings.

"Mister, we're stuck in here – can you let us out?"

He thought about ignoring them – you never know these days – but then he decided he should help and crossed the road.

"What are you doing in there?", he asked.

"They've shut us in", the boy said, "We can't get out".

"What about the side gate back up the road?"

"We can't open it from this side".

He was beginning to regret speaking to them – it was a cold, rainy night and he didn't fancy having to backtrack to the gate. He looked up at the railings that separated them and asked, somewhat unkindly,

"Can't you climb over?"

(They looked fit enough despite the white faces)

"No, mister, we can't", said the girl. "The bits at the top would hurt us"

He looked up at the tips of the railings and the rounded crosses, more like fleur-de-lis, thinking sourly, they don't look all that sharp to me – I bet I could have got over them when I was their age.

The kids looked pleadingly through the railings.

"OK, I'll go back to the gate".

The kids looked triumphant – lucky them he thought, instantly realising that he was now walking into the rain.

As he made his way back to the gate, he suddenly saw a flaw in the plan – he hadn't noticed before, but this gate didn't actually lead directly into the cemetery but into the service yard beside – perhaps those darn kids wouldn't even be able to get there – and then what?

He needn't have worried. When he reached the gate, the kids were already waiting for him. How had they got there so fast? He quickly glanced around the dark yard beyond and could only see walls and buildings on every side.

He opened his mouth to ask them but decided he couldn't be bothered – just let them out and then head home to a warm fire and a hot meal.

The kids looked pretty hungry themselves on the other side of the gate, desperate for him to open it.

He lifted the latch and pulled – it opened easily – why the heck couldn't they have done it for themselves?

He soon realised that the question – and the answer – were the least of his worries.

As they came towards him, eyes glinting and teeth sharp, he knew too late that there are some things you should never let out of a cemetery at night.

NUMBER 13

It was the last drink that did for him – not the previous twelve. He staggered out of the Bear & Staff not at all sure where he was going but some instinct took him towards Weoley Park Road and home.

As he crossed near Lodge Hill Cemetery, he was blinded by the glare of headlights – next thing he knew he was being helped to his feet by a group of people and pushed onto a bus. He tried to tell them that he wasn't going anywhere but it was too late – and he was too drunk – so he just sat down and enjoyed the ride.

He hadn't been on a bus for a while – but this once seemed different, more like the ones he remembered as a child. A middle-aged woman in a nurse's uniform was dabbing his head with a handkerchief: "You people", she said, "Just like that young woman who came off her bike right outside the hospital".

They had been driving for some time now without a stop – he could hardly believe there was a service at all so late at night. Suddenly a voice shouted "Quinton" and they stopped.

Lots of people got off and lots got on – in his drunken stupor it seemed like hundreds. It was like one of those trick shots on TV where an impossible number of people pile into a little car. One bloke looked as half-cut as him, but he had lipstick on his cheek and a satisfied smile on his face.

They took off again and he began dazedly to inspect the passengers nearest to him: an angry 30-something woman in denim, an oldish bloke with an odd, yellowish tint to his face and a man he thought he recognised from when he first got on at Lodge Hill with what looked like two enormous love-bites on his neck.

13
CEMETERY RUN
MOF 225

The next stop was announced as "Key Hill and Warstone Lane". The people who got on here must have been to a fancy-dress party as they were all in Victorian dress. One tallish man wearing a top hat and a monocle gave him a supercilious look in passing.

They drove on for ages, apparently circling the city, judging by the names called out at the infrequent stops: "Handsworth", "Witton", "Sutton Coldfield", "Sutton New Hall" and then, after a very long ride, "Yardley".

He began to wonder if he were on some weird night-time version of the Number 11 Outer Circle – he asked the man next to him, who looked as if he'd been in one hell of a fight – the reply came in a sneering Scottish accent: "Don't be so stupid – it's the Number 13 of course".

The next stop was "Brandwood End". A couple got on there – the woman looking a bit scared of the man – asking if the bus went past "Priory" and someone said it did, on the way to Lodge Hill.

He felt relieved – evidently they'd come all the way round this bizarre circular route and were heading back to where he'd got on. But, before he'd seen anything familiar, the voice shouted "Kings Norton" and the conductor appeared before him: "This is your stop, Sir".

He said he was going to Lodge Hill but the conductor said, "I'm afraid they're full, Sir. This is yours".

Suddenly very sober, he got off the bus and walked through the brand new gates of Kings Norton Cemetery. He looked back as the Number 13 bus drew off and was not at all surprised to see it was an old-style double-decker. He instinctively knew where to go, to the gleaming new headstone with his name on it – like his Mum always said, drinking had been the death of him.